FOOTBALL
maths

PURPLE STRIP

DON SHAW & JOHN SHIELS

You are the manager

_____

Your team name

Colour in your kit

Home kit

Away kit

OXFORD
UNIVERSITY PRESS

How to use this book

The purpose of this series of fill-in workbooks is to give practice in Key Stage 1 and 2 Maths in a motivating context.

The contents list shows which topic of maths is covered on each page, which maths skill this comes under, and at what level. This will give you some indication of how your child might perform in the National Tests.

First of all, your child should decide on their team name, write it in on the title page, and colour their kit in home and away colours. On each page they can decide on a different opponent, and fill in their own team name or colours in the bold framed box and the opposing team in the more lightly framed box. The away games are always slightly harder than the home games.

To work out your child's score, check the number of goals in the answers on page 30, and fill in a result at the foot of each page. Then transfer those results to the table below, and add up the grand total.

Game	Your score	Opponent's score	Win/Lose/Draw
Match results			
p. 4 Home		1	
p. 5 Home		1	
p. 6 Away		0	
p. 7 Home		5	
p. 8 Home		7	
p. 9 Away		1	
p. 10 Home		1	
p. 11 Home		1	
p. 12 Away		1	
p. 13 Home		4	
p. 14 Away		4	
p. 15 Away		0	
p. 16 Home		1	
p. 17 Home		7	
p. 18 Home		0	
p. 19 Home		1	
p. 20 Away		1	
p. 21 Away		1	
p. 22 Home		5	
p. 23 Home		4	
p. 24 Home		4	
p. 25 Away		4	
p. 26 Home		0	
p. 27 Away		1	
p. 28 Home		2	
p. 29 Away		3	
Total		**60**	

CONTENTS

Colour the balls and count how many goals have been scored in these games.

Rovers 4 v Derby 2
○ ○ ○ ○ ○ ○
○ ○ ○ ○ ☐ goals

United 3 v City 1
○ ○ ○ ○
☐ goals

Bury 2 v Athletic 2
○ ○ ○ ○
☐ goals

Ipswich 1 v Villa 4
○ ○ ○ ○ ○
☐ goals

Athletic 5 v Leeds 2
○ ○ ○ ○ ○ ○ ○
☐ goals

Crewe 4 v Rovers 4
○ ○ ○ ○ ○ ○ ○ ○
☐ goals

Chester 3 v Rangers 3
○ ○ ○ ○ ○ ○
☐ goals

United 3 v Norwich 2
○ ○ ○ ○ ○
☐ goals

City 5 v Wrexham 4
○ ○ ○ ○ ○ ○ ○ ○ ○
☐ goals

Rangers 3 v Luton 6
○ ○ ○ ○ ○ ○ ○ ○ ○
☐ goals

What number seats are these people sitting on?

| 26 | 27 | | 29 | 30 |

___

| 95 | 96 | 97 |

___ ___ ___

| 46 | 47 | | 50 | 51 |

___ ___

Join the balls to the goals to make the sums correct.

The first has been done for you.

8		+ 1 = 10
9		+ 4 = 10
5		+ 2 = 10
3		+ 8 = 10
2		+ 5 = 10
6		+ 7 = 10

Work out the sums in the squares.

If the answer is 10 colour it red.

If the answer is not 10 colour it green.

4+5	9+3	7+2	9+2	5+4	2+6	5+7	3+9	6+5	1+8	8+3	3+6	6+2	2+9	6+3	9+3	3+8
2+6	1+9	5+5	4+6	1+8	7+3	6+4	8+2	4+5	3+7	4+6	1+9	5+4	7+3	3+4	4+7	9+2
3+9	8+2	1+7	4+3	2+9	5+5	7+1	6+4	7+4	9+1	7+1	2+8	4+3	9+1	1+7	3+8	4+5
7+1	4+6	8+3	2+8	6+3	8+2	6+2	1+9	3+6	2+8	5+5	8+2	7+2	4+6	5+7	7+4	2+6
3+9	3+7	9+1	6+4	3+4	7+3	2+8	5+5	7+5	7+3	3+4	3+7	9+2	5+5	3+7	1+9	6+5
1+8	5+4	3+6	8+3	7+2	9+3	6+2	1+7	4+7	6+5	2+9	4+8	7+4	3+8	6+3	7+5	4+3

Find a route to goal where the sums add up to 10 each time.

You must follow the direction of the arrows.

When you have found a route to goal colour it in.

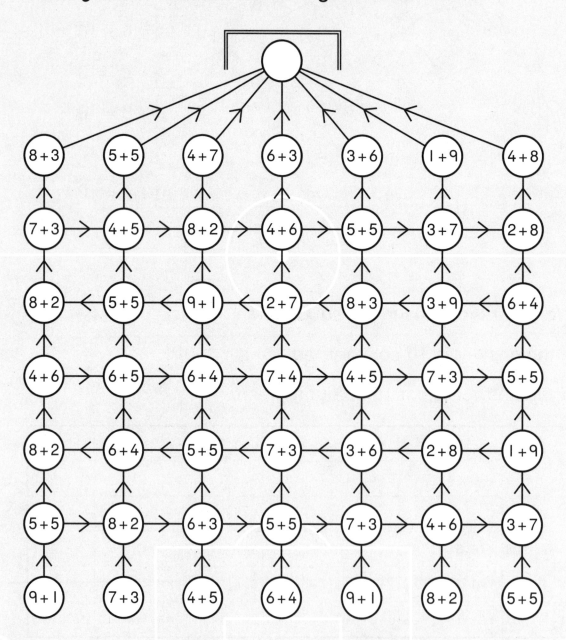

FINAL SCORE

	V	
0		

   V

You have £10 and you buy a poster.

Poster £4

10 – 4 = 6

You have £6 left.

How much will you have left from £10 if you buy these?

You can use your 10 fingers to help you.

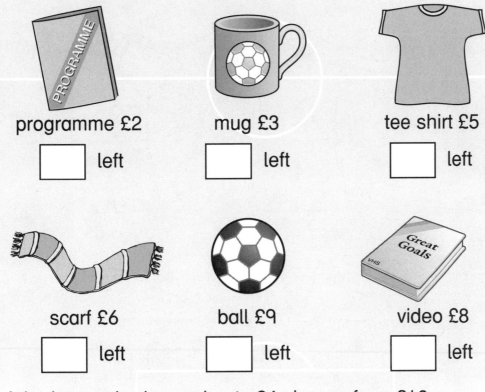

programme £2   ☐ left

mug £3   ☐ left

tee shirt £5   ☐ left

scarf £6   ☐ left

ball £9   ☐ left

video £8   ☐ left

John buys a badge and gets £6 change from £10.

How much did the badge cost? _____

	V	

In each picture the answer on the shirt is the same as the answer on the shorts.

Fill in the missing numbers.

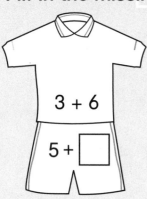 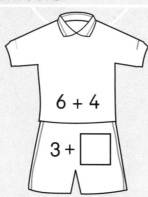 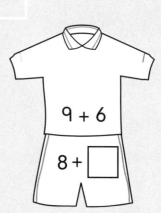

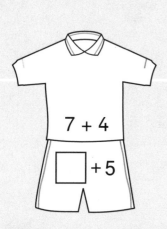 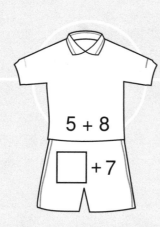 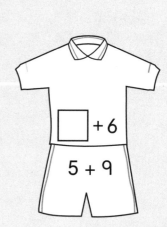

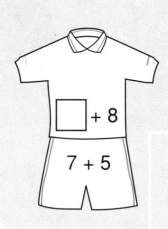 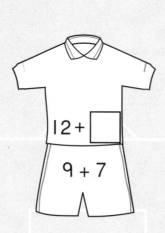 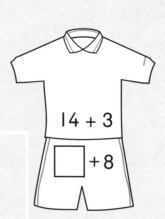

	V	

The goals scored by 5 players

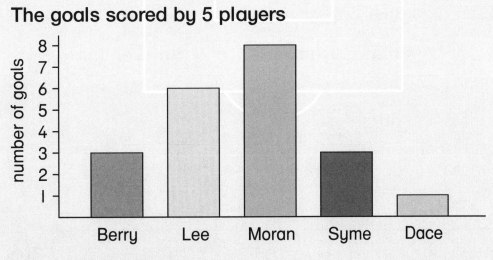

Who scored 6 goals? _____

Who scored the most goals? _____

Which 2 players scored the same goals? _____

Who scored the fewest goals? _____

The cups won by 4 teams in the last ten years

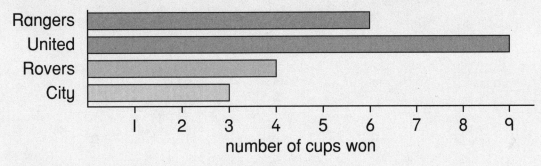

How many cups have United won? _____

How many cups have Rovers won? _____

Who has won 2 more cups than Rovers? _____

Who has won 3 fewer cups than United? _____

Who has won twice as many cups as City? _____

V

All numbers are either odd or even.

The odd numbers are above this line and the even numbers are below it.

Fill in the missing numbers.

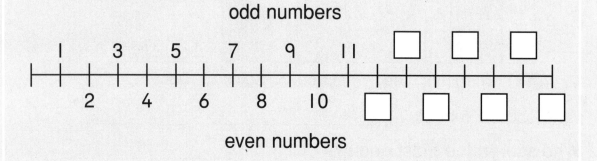

odd numbers

1   3   5   7   9   11   ☐   ☐   ☐

2   4   6   8   10   ☐   ☐   ☐   ☐

even numbers

Colour the odd numbers green and the even numbers yellow.

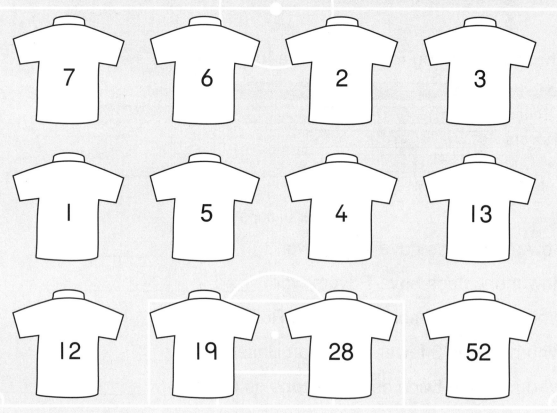

7   6   2   3

1   5   4   13

12   19   28   52

For each player make up an addition sum that equals the shirt number.

The first has been done for you.

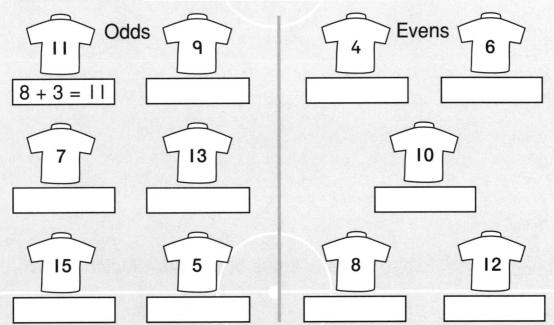

Odds

11 — 8 + 3 = 11

9 — [ ]

Evens

4 — [ ]

6 — [ ]

7 — [ ]

13 — [ ]

10 — [ ]

15 — [ ]

5 — [ ]

8 — [ ]

12 — [ ]

Colour the even numbers red and the odd numbers green.

What extra pieces of kit do you then find?

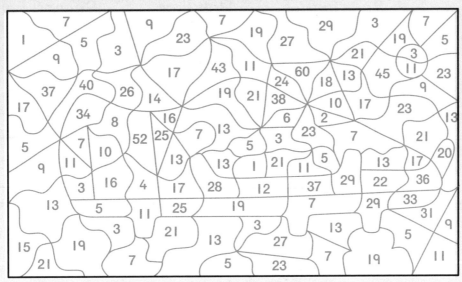

Fill in your teams

[   ] V [   ]

Draw the hands on the clocks and follow Rachel's special day out watching your team play away.

8 o'clock
Wake up

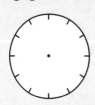

9 o'clock
Get up

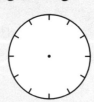

9.30
Breakfast

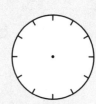

10 o'clock
Watch T.V.

12.30
Lunch

1.15
Leave home

2 o'clock
Arrive at ground

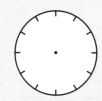

3 o'clock
Match starts

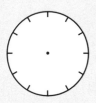

3.15
Opponents
score 0–1

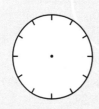

3.30
Your team
score

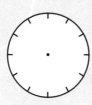

3.45
Half-time

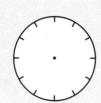

4 o'clock
Second half
begins

4.15
Your team
scores 2–1

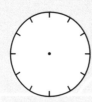

4.30
Your team
score 3–1

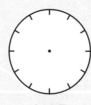

4.45
Full-time

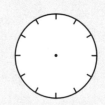

6 o'clock
Arrive home

FINAL SCORE

[   ] I V [   ]

There are 7 balls in a bag but 3 fall out.

7 − 3 = 4

There are 4 balls left in the bag.

Write how many balls are left in these bags.

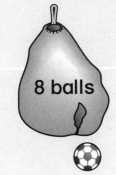

□ − □ = □   □ − □ = □   □ − □ = □

□ − □ = □   □ − □ = □   □ − □ = □

FINAL SCORE

V   4

Liverpool have 15 players.

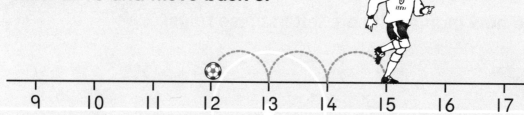

3 are injured.

15 − 3 = 12

12 are left to play.

You can use a number line to work out this sum.

Start at 15 and move back 3.

9   10   11   12   13   14   15   16   17

Work out how many players these teams have left who are fit.

Chelsea 16 players 2 injured ▢ fit	Everton 17 players 4 injured ▢ fit	Villa 14 players 3 injured ▢ fit
Leeds 15 players 4 injured ▢ fit	Newcastle 16 players 5 injured ▢ fit	United 15 players 6 injured ▢ fit

FINAL SCORE

4

	V	

If you want to work out the difference between 13 and 10, you can use a number line like this.

This is the difference between 11 and 7.

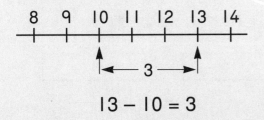

$$13 - 10 = 3$$

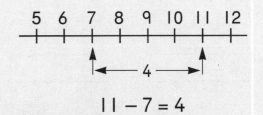

$$11 - 7 = 4$$

Use the number line to work out the differences and colour in the picture.

Difference	Colour
2	Green
3	Yellow
4	Red
5	Black

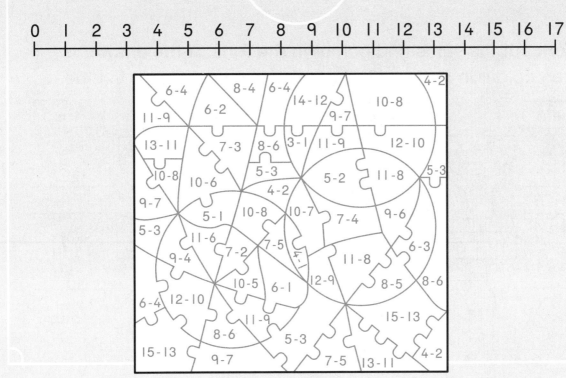

FINAL SCORE

	0	V	

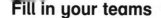

[   ] V [   ]

For each player make up a subtraction sum that equals the shirt number.

The first one has been done for you.

| 11 | 3 | 10 | 5 |

| 14 − 3 = 11 | [   ] | [   ] | [   ] |

| 9 | 1 | 6 |

| [   ] | [   ] | [   ] |

| 7 | 2 | 8 | 4 |

| [   ] | [   ] | [   ] | [   ] |

Work out the sums and colour in the fans. If the answer is even colour in red, and if the answer is odd colour in blue.

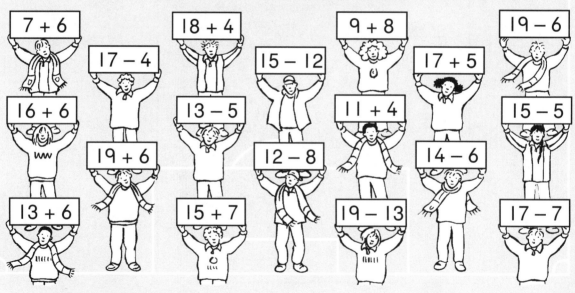

7 + 6   18 + 4   9 + 8   19 − 6
17 − 4   15 − 12   17 + 5
16 + 6   13 − 5   11 + 4   15 − 5
19 + 6   12 − 8   14 − 6
13 + 6   15 + 7   19 − 13   17 − 7

FINAL SCORE

[|] V [| 1]

These angles are called right-angles.

Colour the shapes which contain right-angles red and the other shapes blue.

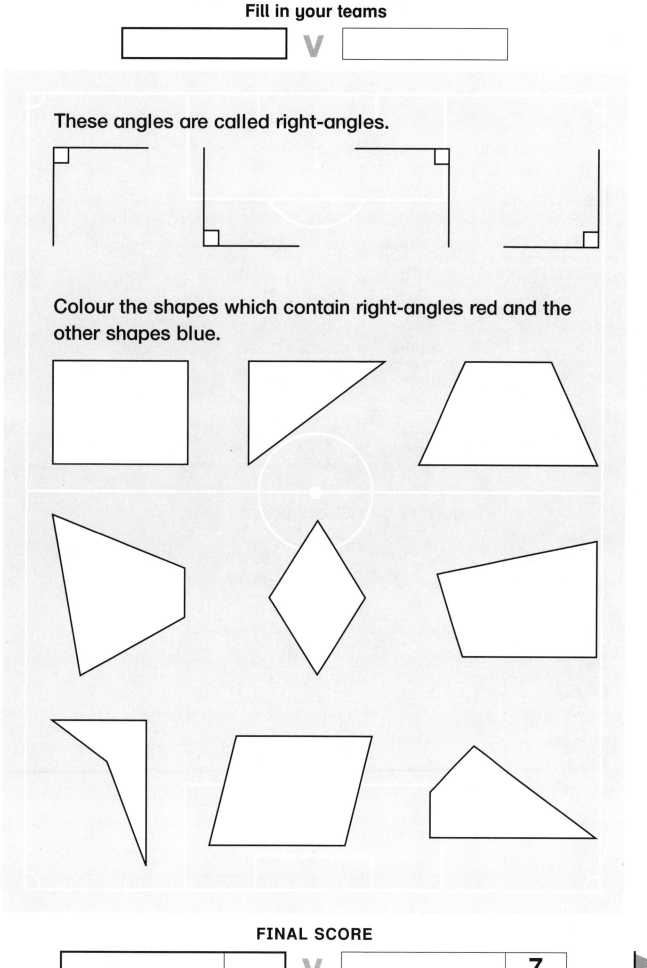

	V	

Fill in the table below by matching the players with the number of goals scored. One has been done for you.

Smith
23 goals

Jones
47 goals

Hamer
51 goals

Webb
94 goals

Parr
68 goals

Watson
89 goals

Rogers
49 goals

Cope
35 goals

Hardy
72 goals

Gray
16 goals

Player	Goals scored
	sixteen
Smith	twenty-three
	thirty-five
	forty-seven
	forty-nine
	fifty-one
	sixty-eight
	seventy-two
	eighty-nine
	ninety-four

FINAL SCORE

	V	0

V

Tick the flags that have one half shaded.

✔

Tick the flags that have one quarter shaded.

✔

Goals scored by 5 players

John	● ● ● ● ●
Pete	● ● ● ● ● ●
Dave	● ● ● ●
Steve	● ● ● ● ● ● ●
Ian	● ●

John scored 5 goals.

Pete scored _____ goals.

Who scored the most goals? _____

Who scored the least goals? _____

Who scored twice as many as Ian? _____

Cups won by 6 managers

Murray	🏆 🏆 🏆
Wilkins	🏆 🏆 🏆 🏆 🏆
Palmer	🏆 🏆 🏆 🏆
Tyrie	🏆 🏆 🏆 🏆 🏆
Ridley	🏆 🏆 🏆 🏆 🏆 🏆 🏆 🏆
Adams	🏆 🏆 🏆 🏆 🏆 🏆

Adams has won 6 cups.

Wilkins has won _____ cups.

Murray has won _____ cups.

Palmer has won _____ cups.

Who has won the most cups? _____

Which 2 managers have won the same number of cups? _____

Which manager has won half as many cups as Adams? _____

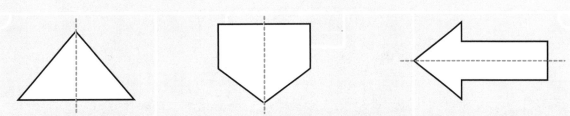

The above shapes are all symmetrical, which means they can be divided into 2 reflected parts.

The dotted line is called a line of symmetry.

Colour the symmetrical shapes red and the other shapes green.

Draw a line of symmetry on each red shape.

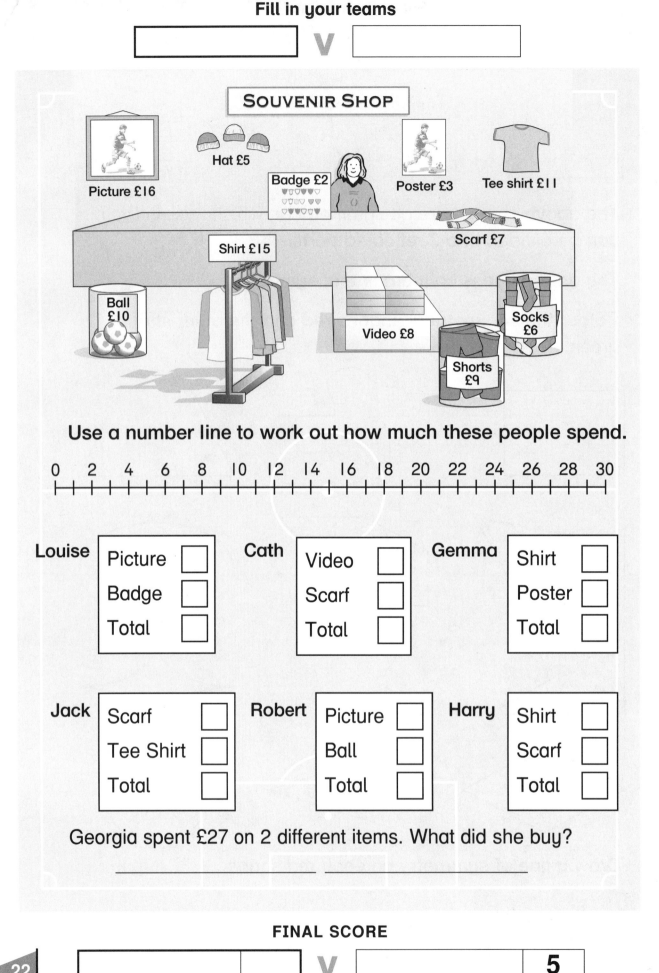

SOUVENIR SHOP

Picture £16

Hat £5

Badge £2

Poster £3

Tee shirt £11

Scarf £7

Shirt £15

Ball £10

Video £8

Shorts £9

Socks £6

Use a number line to work out how much these people spend.

0 2 4 6 8 10 12 14 16 18 20 22 24 26 28 30

Louise
Picture	
Badge	
Total	

Cath
Video	
Scarf	
Total	

Gemma
Shirt	
Poster	
Total	

Jack
Scarf	
Tee Shirt	
Total	

Robert
Picture	
Ball	
Total	

Harry
Shirt	
Scarf	
Total	

Georgia spent £27 on 2 different items. What did she buy?

_____   _____

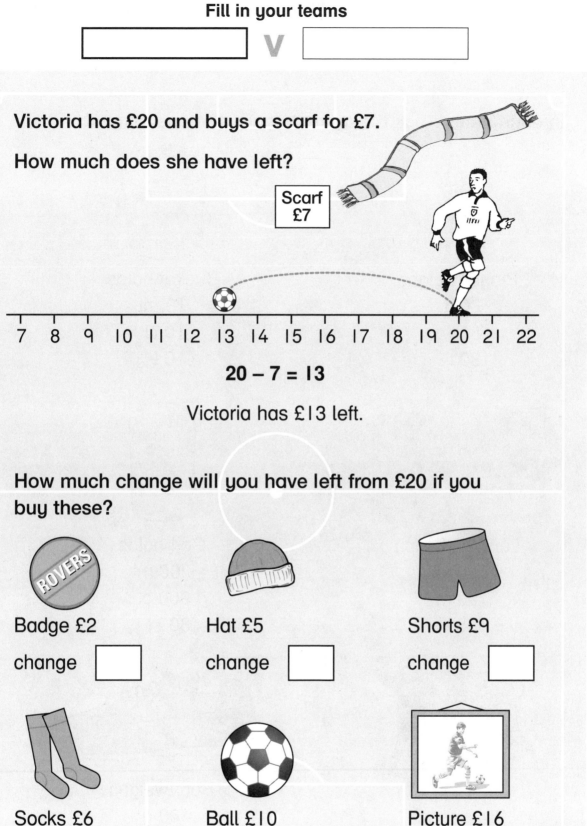

Victoria has £20 and buys a scarf for £7.

How much does she have left?

Scarf £7

7 8 9 10 11 12 13 14 15 16 17 18 19 20 21 22

20 – 7 = 13

Victoria has £13 left.

How much change will you have left from £20 if you buy these?

Badge £2

change ☐

Hat £5

change ☐

Shorts £9

change ☐

Socks £6

change ☐

Ball £10

change ☐

Picture £16

change ☐

FINAL SCORE

V   4

	V	

In each picture tick the correct scale of measurement.

Player weighs
80 g
80 kg
80 t

Bucket holds
10 ml
10 cl
10 l

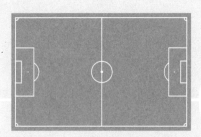

Length of pitch
100 cm
100 m
100 km

Can holds
300 ml
300 cl
300 l

Match lasts
90 seconds
90 minutes
90 hours

Boot weighs
400 g
400 kg
400 t

FINAL SCORE

		V		4

V

Katie has 3 shots at a target wall.

She scores   8 + 4 + 3

8	3	9
4	2	5
6	1	7

Katie scores 15 points

0 1 2 3 4 5 6 7 8 9 10 11 12 13 14 15 16

1 Work out how many points these players score.

8	3	9
4	2	5
6	1	7

Daniel scores ☐

8	3	9
4	2	5
6	1	7

Rachel scores ☐

8	3	9
4	2	5
6	1	7

Shaun scores ☐

8	3	9
4	2	5
6	1	7

Jessica scores ☐

8	3	9
4	2	5
6	1	7

Thomas scores ☐

8	3	9
4	2	5
6	1	7

Helena scores ☐

2 Who got the highest score? _____

3 Who got the lowest score? _____

4 Write down 2 different ways that you could score 17.

_____ _____

5 If Jonathan hits 3 different numbers what is the highest score that he can get?

FINAL SCORE

4   V

25

	V	

Fill in the table by writing in words the goals scored by each player.

The first one has been done for you.

Rogers
41 goals

Lau
65 goals

Jones
54 goals

Thomas
39 goals

Day
27 goals

Bailey
78 goals

Lock
18 goals

Hulme
87 goals

Key
93 goals

Parr
62 goals

West
34 goals

Owen
43 goals

Players	Goals scored	Players	Goals scored
Rogers	forty-one	Lock	
Lau		Hulme	
Jones		Key	
Thomas		Parr	
Day		West	
Bailey		Owen	

FINAL SCORE

		V		0

[_____] **V** [_____]

I Find the 6 football boots hidden in the picture below.

2 Work out the sums and colour in the picture.

Answer	Colour
12	Yellow
13	Brown
14	Black
15	Light blue
16	Pink
17	Red
18	Green

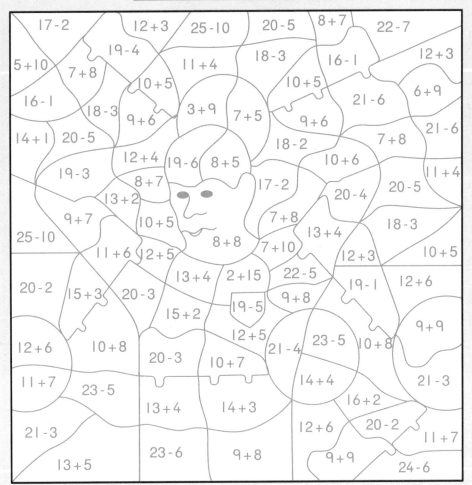

FINAL SCORE

[_____] **I** **V** [_____]

Fill in the table, starting with the player who has scored the fewest goals.

Todd	Hill	Hughes
46 goals	70 goals	84 goals

Clegg	Bell	East
29 goals	17 goals	47 goals

Jones	Webb	Roberts
54 goals	38 goals	61 goals

Goals scored	Players
17	Bell

Work out the sums on the shirts, then fill in the names in order on the team sheet. The first has been done for you.

Cope
12 − 9
3

Smith
10 − 2

Jones
8 − 3

Morris
19 − 18

Rogers
11 − 5

Gray
15 − 5

Parr
13 − 6

Evans
13 − 4

Hamer
17 − 13

Webb
17 − 15

Hunt
14 − 3

Team Sheet

1	
2	
3	Cope
4	
5	

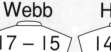

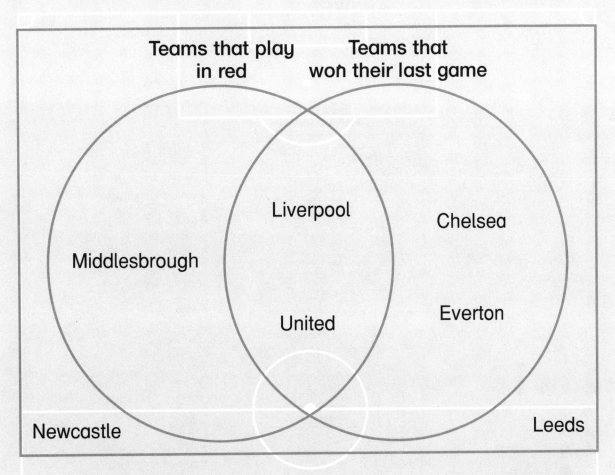

Teams that play in red   **Teams that won their last game**

Middlesbrough

Liverpool

Chelsea

United

Everton

Newcastle

Leeds

1 Which two teams play in red and also won their last game?

_____   _____

2 Which team plays in red but did not win their last game?

_____

3 Name a team that do not play in red but who won their last game. _____

4 Why is Leeds outside both circles? _____

5 If Tottenham play in white and they won their last game place them on the diagram. _____

▶ PAGE **4**

6, 4, 4, 5, 7, 8, 6, 5, 9, 9
28; 48, 49; 98, 99, 100
Maximum score 2 goals

▶ PAGE **5**

8 + 2 = 10
9 + 1 = 10
5 + 5 = 10
3 + 7 = 10
2 + 8 = 10
6 + 4 = 10

The word GOAL should appear in red
Maximum score 2 goals.

▶ PAGE **6**

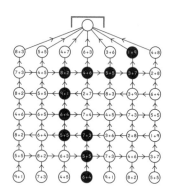

There may be other possible solutions.
Maximum score 1 goal.

▶ PAGE **7**

£8   £7   £5
£4   £1   £2

The badge cost £4.
Maximum score 7 goals.

▶ PAGE **8**

4   7   7
6   6   8
4   4   9

Maximum score 9 goals.

▶ PAGE **9**

Lee   Moran   Berry & Syme   Dace
9
4
Rangers
Rangers
Rangers

Maximum score 2 goals.

▶ PAGE **10**

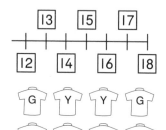

Maximum score 2 goals.

▶ PAGE **11**

There are many possible answers.

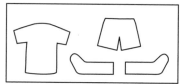

Maximum score 2 goals.

▶ PAGE **12**

Maximum score 3 goals.

▶ PAGE **13**

8 − 1 = 7   5 − 3 = 2   8 − 2 = 6
7 − 4 = 3   6 − 3 = 3   9 − 5 = 4
Maximum score 6 goals.

▶ PAGE **14**

14   13   11
11   11   9
Maximum score 6 goals.

▶ PAGE **15**

Maximum score 1 goal.

▶ PAGE **16**

There are many possible solutions

B   R   B   B
     B   B   R
R   R   B   R
B   R   R
B   R   R   R

Maximum score 2 goals.

▶ PAGE **17**

R   R   B
B   B   R
R   B   R

Maximum score 9 goals.

▶ PAGE **18**

Gray
Smith
Cope
Jones
Rogers
Hamer
Parr
Hardy
Watson
Webb

Maximum score 1 goal.

▶ PAGE **19**

✓   ✓   ✗   ✓   ✗
✗   ✓   ✓   ✗   ✓

✓   ✗   ✗   ✗
✓   ✗   ✗   ✓

Maximum score 2 goals.

▶ PAGE **20**

6
Steve
Ian
Dave

5 cups
3 cups
4 cups
Ridley
Wilkins and Tyrie
Murray

Maximum score 2 goals.

▶ PAGE 21

```
R  G  R
G  G  R
G  G  R
R  R  R
```

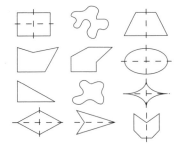

Maximum score 2 goals.

▶ PAGE 22

16	8	15	7	16	15
2	7	3	11	10	7
18	15	18	18	26	22

Georgia bought a Tee-shirt and a picture.

Maximum score 7 goals.

▶ PAGE 23

£18   £15   £11   £14   £10   £4

Maximum score 6 goals.

▶ PAGE 24

80 kg	10 l	100 m
300 ml	90 minutes	400 g

Maximum score 6 goals.

▶ PAGE 25

```
15   13   15
18   16   19
```
Helena
Rachel
1,9,7 or 2,9,6 or 2,8,7 or 3,9,5 or 3,8,6
or 4,8,5 or 4,7,6
24

Maximum score 5 goals.

▶ PAGE 26

Rogers	forty-one
Lau	sixty-five
Jones	fifty-four
Thomas	thirty-nine
Day	twenty-seven
Bailey	seventy-eight
Lock	eighteen
Hulme	eighty-seven
Key	ninety-three
Parr	sixty-two
West	thirty-four
Owen	forty-three

Maximum score 1 goal.

▶ PAGE 27

6 boots hidden

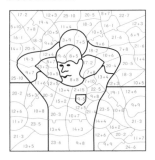

Maximum score 1 goal.

▶ PAGE 28

Goals scored	Players
17	Bell
29	Clegg
38	Webb
46	Todd
47	East
54	Jones
61	Roberts
70	Hill
84	Hughes

1 Morris
2 Webb
3 Cope
4 Hamer
5 Jones
6 Rogers
7 Parr
8 Smith
9 Evans
10 Gray
11 Hunt

Maximum score 3 goals.

▶ PAGE 29

Liverpool   United
Middlesbrough
Chelsea or Everton

They do not play in red and they did not win their last game.

Tottenham should be placed in the same region as Chelsea and Everton.

Maximum score 5 goals.

Bobby Charlton Soccer Schools
'Learning through Football'

Special School courses are available at the Bobby Charlton Soccer School HQ in Manchester throughout the year, either residentially or non residential. All participants will be able to tackle the problems of Key Stage 2 Maths and English, as well as receive expert tuition putting them through their soccer paces. There will also be an opportunity to visit the great Manchester attractions of Manchester United FC and Granada Tours. For further details contact John Shiels at Bobby Charlton Sports School, Hopwood Hall, Rochdale Road, Middleton, Manchester, M24 6XH or Telephone: 0161 643 3113 Fax: 0161 643 1444.

Individual courses in Maths and football are available each Easter vacation.

OXFORD
UNIVERSITY PRESS

Great Clarendon Street, Oxford OX2 6DP

Oxford New York
Athens Auckland Bangkok Bogotá Bombay Buenos Aires Calcutta
Cape Town Dar es Salaam Delhi Florence Hong Kong Istanbul
Karachi Kuala Lumpur Madrid Melbourne Mexico City Mumbai
Nairobi Paris São Paulo Singapore Taipei Tokyo Toronto Warsaw

and associated companies in Berlin Ibadan

Oxford is a registered trade mark of Oxford University Press

© Oxford University Press 1999
First published 1999

ISBN 019 838232 4

Typeset and designed by Oxprint Design, Oxford

Printed in Hong Kong

Cover photograph by The Image Bank/Chris Cole